The VSED Handbook: A Practical Guide to Voluntarily Stopping Eating and Drinking

by Kate Christie

DEDICATION

To my beautiful mother, a pioneer in life and death, and to my father, who showed grace, love, and courage in supporting her decision to leave on her own terms.

TABLE OF CONTENTS

FOREWORD BY NANCY SIMMERS   1

INTRODUCTION   3

PREPARING FOR VSED   14

    THE DECISION   16
    WHEN TO START   17
    WHERE TO DIE   18
    DOCUMENTATION   19
    HOSPICE CARE SUPPORT   22
    MEDICAL SUPPORT   23
    DEATH DOULA   25
    PAID CAREGIVERS   26
    VSED SUPPLIES   27
    COMFORT MEASURES   28
    SAYING GOODBYE   29
    AFTER-DEATH PLANS   30

FINAL VSED PREP   32

STOPPING EATING AND DRINKING   38

    EARLY PHASE   41
    MIDDLE PHASE   44
    LATE PHASE   46

FAST-FORWARDING DEMENTIA   49

SURVIVOR GUILT AND THE IMPORTANCE OF SELF-CARE   51

VSED, CAPACITY, AND FAMILY FRACTURE   54

    THE QUESTION OF LEGALITY   54
    TWO TYPES OF CAPACITY   55
    FAMILY FRACTURE   57

APPENDIX A: ALL THE TIPS   60

APPENDIX B: VSED TIMELINE   63

APPENDIX C: VSED STATEMENT   65

APPENDIX D: VALUES WORKSHEET   68

APPENDIX E: OTHER RESOURCES   71

YOUR NOTES   73

ABOUT THE AUTHOR   76

ACKNOWLEDGMENTS

Without Nancy Simmers, death doula extraordinaire, and the compassionate caregiving team she put together (Andrea, Joan, and Beth), my mother Jane wouldn't have achieved the good death she sought through VSED—nor would this book exist. I also want to thank my aunts, cousins, in-laws, and family friends for their love and support of Mom's wishes. I owe particular thanks to my wife Kris for her steadfast support as well as to Charlotte, Ed, and Barb, who flew to Washington to be present for Mom's VSED process. Lastly, my family would like to thank our local hospice care organization, Mom's physician, and our attorney Erin Mae Glass for supporting her decision to write a peaceful ending to the story of her life. It takes a village, and we were lucky to have a dedicated, loving team to support us before, during, and after Mom's death.

FOREWORD BY NANCY SIMMERS

Before I heard the call to be a death doula, I was a birth doula who, for many decades, gave emotional and physical support to women as they birthed new life. Now, as a death doula, I am attuned to the many similarities between birth and death. Both are physical, emotional, and spiritual experiences. Both are transitions. Both benefit from nurturing emotional support, shared information, tender physical care, and open-hearted witnessing.

What I've learned from being at the bedside of many who have hastened their death by voluntarily stopping eating and drinking (VSED) is that every VSED experience is as unique to the individual as birth. I've also learned that—as Kate Christie reminds us in *The VSED Handbook*—the VSED process is more similar to a marathon than a sprint. Preparation is critically important to achieve a VSED experience that is orderly, relatively comfortable, confidently undertaken, and compassionately held.

In early 2020, I was privileged to help Kate's mother Jane achieve just such a VSED experience. Like others who have chosen VSED, Jane was a pioneer. The American healthcare system is still reluctant to support VSED, despite the fact it is the one end-of-life choice that is available to residents of every state in the country. While physician awareness is expanding through palliative care programs and hospice, people continue to suffer and, unfortunately, sometimes resort to ending their lives violently. And so the circles of suffering and grief expand to families and beyond, rippling out into the broader community.

In the pages ahead, Kate beautifully recounts her family's experiences with VSED while providing a comprehensive plan for anyone considering hastening their death. Decades ago, in the early 1970s, pregnant women in the United States began to reclaim childbirth as a natural, human event rather than a medical procedure. As the same generation of women and men are aging, they are similarly reclaiming dying as a natural event in which the individual has the final say in how they die—when, where, and in whose presence.

You hold in your hands a worthy guidebook for contemplating your own end-of-life choices. May you find in it the words and stories, suggestions and lessons that will help guide you on your path.

Nancy A. Simmers, BSN, RN, Death Doula
Coordinator, VSED Resources Northwest
March 2022

INTRODUCTION

The sun was setting outside my parents' Western Washington condo on an unseasonably warm day in early 2020 when I heard the words I'd simultaneously been hoping for and dreading: "She's going."

"What?" I asked, somehow startled despite the fact my mother had lapsed into a coma two days earlier.

"She's going," Beth, the nurse, repeated gently. "It's time to say goodbye."

I'd been waiting for this moment for several days, but now that it was here, it seemed rushed and incomplete, too soon and yet far too long in coming. I felt like an actor in a scene that couldn't possibly be real life as I stepped closer to my mother's bedside and touched her soft, fine hair, brushing it aside so that I could kiss her cool forehead.

"Goodbye, Mom," I murmured while Beth and my father-in-law left the room to find my father. "I love you. Thank you for my life. Fly away free."

A moment later, Dad returned and dropped to his knees at my mother's bedside, clasping one of her hands in both of his. "Jane," he said, his voice ragged. "Oh, Jane…"

I ducked out into the hallway, looking for my aunt, Charlotte, who had stepped away only a few minutes before. By the time I found her and brought her back, it was over. My mother was gone. As Charlotte kissed Mom's forehead and Nancy, our death doula, lit a candle on the bedside table, I moved to the other side of the hospital bed and collapsed to my knees, burying my face in the blanket covering my mother's legs. There, I held her thin hand and cried wordlessly, finally letting loose the great sobs I'd mostly managed to hold back through the ten days it took her to die.

She had done it. I couldn't quite believe that she had actually done it. After a decade of suffering while dementia robbed her of vitality, cognition, and memories, she had voluntarily stopped eating and drinking. Ten days later, she was gone.

A few minutes after Mom stopped breathing, a bald eagle that had been hanging around our Western Washington neighborhood took flight from the trees near my parents' condo, arcing up into the sky and flying away across the nearby lake.

I like to think my mother's spirit was with that eagle, flying away free.

~

"I don't want to die a stranger among strangers," Mom told me shortly before she began the process of voluntarily stopping eating and drinking (VSED). "I don't want to die angry and restrained. Because that's how it will be for me. I know it will."

Almost everyone who knew my mother recognized that her fate in a memory care unit would likely not be easy. Jane was a strong, intelligent woman who had marched on Washington for women's rights more than once, helped found a scholarship for working mothers, and regularly climbed mountains in Wyoming throughout her fifties and sixties. Whenever someone called her a lady, she would correct them: "I'm no lady. I'm a woman." She'd always been quick to anger, but when she was diagnosed with

4

cognitive impairment in the late 2000s, her emotional reactivity gradually began to worsen.

In 2019, after a long, slow slide into dementia, Mom began to demonstrate increasing aggression and combative behavior in what would end up being the last full year of her life. We all understood that if Mom were to be committed to a memory care facility against her wishes, there was a strong chance she would be sedated in order to protect herself and others. And not just for a little while. She would likely remain sedated until her disease reached a stage where she was no longer aggressive. By then, dementia would have stolen more than Mom's rage. It would have stolen the core of what made her the fiercely independent person she was.

"If you put me in a nursing home, I will come back and haunt you," my mother told me more than once over the last two decades of her life. She wasn't joking, either. Institutionalized care frightened her because she hated the idea of being physically vulnerable and out of control among strangers tasked with acting in her best interests. She didn't want a memory care facility's version of "safety." She wanted to be able to leave this world on her own terms while she was still herself. Memory care wasn't a last-ditch option, as far as she was concerned. It simply wasn't an option at all.

And yet, that was the only end-of-life choice my mother was offered by the mainstream medical establishment: steady, agonizing cognitive decline until she could no longer live at home and was forced against her will into a memory care facility. There, she would likely be sedated and restrained while she languished from a terrible disease, slowly forgetting every experience she'd ever had—and every person she'd ever loved. There was always the chance she might contract pneumonia or some other illness that would kill her faster than Alzheimer's, but it was just as likely she wouldn't. She was physically strong from a lifetime of outdoor activity, and there was no way to predict how long the late stages of dementia would take. No way to say how far she might ultimately fall.

Would Mom end up like our family friend who had no idea who her husband and children were? Would she end up like her own mother, my grandmother, who spent seven years in a memory care ward before her body finally succumbed? Seven years as a stranger among strangers—to my mom, the idea of following in her mother's final footsteps was too painful to contemplate.

"You'll have to give up good days," our attorney Erin—an advocate for death with dignity in general and VSED in particular—cautioned in late 2016 when my mother first met with her to discuss VSED as a potential early exit from Alzheimer's. My parents had recently attended an event called "Death Happens," sponsored by the Palliative Care Institute at Western Washington University. There, they learned that people suffering from dementia and other cognitive disorders are not eligible for medical aid in dying (MAID) under Washington State's MAID statute. They also heard Phyllis Shacter, a VSED advocate, describe her late husband Alan's experience after he decided to hasten his own death to avoid the end stages of Alzheimer's disease. Mom had decided then and there that she wanted to do the same thing—when the time was right, of course.

That was the most difficult part of VSED for my parents: choosing the right time for Mom to stop eating and drinking.

The person with dementia, Erin explained at her first meeting with my parents, has to time their VSED start date just right. Voluntarily stopping eating and drinking requires a level of mental and emotional fortitude typically absent in later stages of dementia. That means a person suffering from Alzheimer's disease can't wait until they've lost so much cognitive function that they're unable to complete the VSED process. To reach her goal of dying with dignity, Erin said, Mom would have to be prepared to give up good days to avoid bad years.

Give up good days to avoid bad years—for Mom, that trade-off was acceptable. For others in the family, much less so. When Mom suggested a potential start date of summer 2017, Dad refused to consider it. Mom didn't push, and in hindsight, I fully believe Dad was right about the timing. We ended up getting two more years of nature walks, soccer practices and games, Friday night movie nights, and holidays with Mom that we wouldn't have experienced otherwise. When it mattered, when she began to near a cognitive point of no return, Dad supported her wish to do VSED—even though it meant losing his life partner of 55 years.

Despite the wait, Mom did have to give up good days. At the time she and Dad picked for her to begin VSED, Mom could still enjoy Sunday morning brunch with the whole family; still play charades and Monopoly with my school-aged children; still enjoy concerts and movies; still sing silly songs and decorate holiday cookies and watch the kids ride their bikes around her and Dad's condo complex. But because of sundowning—dementia-related agitation, irritability, and confusion that often kicked in as daylight began to fade—and her increased combativeness and fall risk, she couldn't enjoy family pizza and movie nights anymore or go on day trips to the ocean or the mountains with us. Because of her accelerating cognitive decline, she couldn't read a book or bake cookies or take care of her garden or drive her beloved red truck. Her bold, adventurous life had eroded into a shadow existence, marked by a series of increasingly rapid losses that she could neither halt nor abide by.

"I'm always aware of the disease," she told me the

morning she started VSED. "It's like losing pieces of yourself that you can never get back. I can feel it getting faster, too, the past month especially. That's why I know this is the right time to leave. Don't get me wrong—I would love to stick around for another six months. But I think I'll always feel that way, and if we wait, I don't know what will happen. I don't know if I would be able to do VSED in another six months, or even next month. It has to be now."

As someone who had lived a full life on her own terms, she couldn't bear the thought of becoming what she called "an old lady walking the halls of a nursing home" not knowing who—or where—she was.

Fortunately, she didn't have to.

On February 1, 2020, my mother voluntarily stopped eating and drinking. Ten days later, she died in what had once been her home office, her hospital bed facing the lake, one eye partially open in her final moments as if she wanted to see her family, her life, her world one last time before flying away, free from dementia at last.

~

I am not a medical professional. Let's get that out of the way now. I'm also not a legal professional. What I am is the daughter of a courageous woman who made the plan to die on her own terms and then carried out that plan, even though it meant leaving the family she adored. Even though it meant giving up good days with her loving husband who she'd spent her entire adult life with; even though it meant missing out on special times with her sisters and their children, with her own family, and, especially, with her grandchildren. She was willing to give up those moments because she had already been losing those things for years. By the time she set her VSED plan in motion, she had been ill with—and suffering from—an untreatable terminal disease marked by steady cognitive decline for more than a decade.

As our local hospice care nursing manager said, "Jane didn't choose a terminal illness. She only chose not to let the disease pick when and how she would die. She wanted to determine how the last chapter of her life would unfold, and so she chose an ending to the story of her life that was right for her."

We were lucky. The hospice care organization in our area of Western Washington supported my mother's choice to hasten her own death. That's actually my first tip for anyone looking into VSED for themselves or a loved one: Call your local hospice care organization and find out if they support VSED. Because if they do, many things will be easier. And if they say they don't, refuse to take no for an answer. My mom's case was one of the first to receive official approval in our area, and then only in the last half of her VSED process. Now, thanks to my mom's pioneering efforts, our local Hospice supports VSED patients—and their family members—from the beginning of their fast onward.

Be the change you want to see, as they say. My mother certainly was.

Of course, none of that change would have been possible without the support team we assembled: our family attorney, Mom and Dad's physician, the local hospice facility, in-home nurses, members of our extended family, and the amazing death doula we were able to bring on board the month before Mom started VSED.

That's my next big tip: Hire a death doula if possible and assemble a team of folks to support your dying process who are experienced with VSED. Finding those people can be difficult. Your doula might be able to help; ours did.

Alternately, if you live in a state where medical aid in dying (MAID) is legal, contact the organization responsible for overseeing the medicated dying process and ask if they know of VSED professionals in your region. Sometimes that organization will support VSED themselves. For example, End of Life Washington has expanded their services to include those who choose VSED.

If you don't live in a state where MAID is legal, there might be an advocacy group in your area working to advance the cause of death with dignity in your state's legislature. Contact them—they may be able to connect you with progressive legal or medical professionals in your area. You can also try an Internet search for the local/state branch of Compassion and Choices (formerly the Hemlock Society). They are often aligned with a progressive network and might know of folks with VSED experience.

The fact is, managing a VSED death without professional support is difficult, if not impossible. The process isn't easy or fast. Like running a marathon, VSED takes significant planning and coordination to complete. Which brings me to another big tip: Having adequate support both for the dying person *and* their loved ones is crucial to avoid unnecessary physical and emotional suffering. That doesn't mean there won't be suffering. Dying is difficult, and losing a loved one is painful. But for my mom, facing an uncertain road with an insidious disease and denied access to medical aid in dying, VSED was the least bad end-of-life choice she felt she could make.

My wife and I tell our children frequently that teamwork makes the dream work. For my mom, the dream consisted of a good death on her own terms before dementia robbed her of every last thing that made her who she was. Thanks to her determination and strength of will—and the team of loved ones and hired caregivers we assembled—she achieved that dream.

"I would call this a very good death," the social worker from hospice said the day before Mom died.

"Really?" I asked. "I mean, I guess you see that a lot."

She gazed at me steadily. "Not as often as you might think."

To be honest, I didn't believe a peaceful death from VSED was possible before I witnessed it. I supported my mother's choice from the start, but privately I was horrified by her decision to dehydrate herself to death. As the days and nights passed, though, my perspective shifted. By the end, I'd come to realize that VSED didn't have to be the horrible death by dehydration I had imagined. For Mom, it was the peaceful, meaningful end to a life well lived.

That's one of the main messages of this book: A good death from VSED is possible—*if* you understand what death from dehydration entails, prepare accordingly, and surround yourself with a committed, experienced team. Other than medical aid in dying, VSED can be one of the fastest, most painless ways to hasten death, assuming the patient receives adequate medical support.

That brings up another tip: Use palliative care medicines as early as possible to ease suffering. VSED takes an average of ten to fourteen days, but the process can last anywhere from several days to several weeks. Managing palliative medication levels properly can mean the difference between a peaceful death and a harrowing one.

VSED isn't a cheap end-of-life option. As a result, it's still mostly chosen and carried out by people of privilege—those who own or have access to a private home setting for two or three weeks; those who can afford a death doula and private caregivers; those who have the means to rent hospital equipment and pay for palliative care medications. My hope is that as VSED becomes a more accepted end-of-life choice, a growing infrastructure might make it more accessible to anyone with a terminal or progressive disease who chooses to hasten their death.

In the meantime, I offer you this book.

The goal of *The VSED Handbook* is to provide an actionable model for how to go about planning for and carrying out VSED, with the aim of achieving the type of peaceful passing my mother did. In the pages ahead, I'll provide details about preparing for VSED as well as an overview of what the process itself entails, supplementing the process-oriented sections with what I hope are relevant examples from my family's experience. I'll also highlight tips that I would have found useful while helping Mom prepare for and carry out VSED; but if you miss any, don't worry—I'll list all the tips from each section at the end of the book for easy reference, along with a VSED timeline, a copy of my mother's VSED statement, a medical values worksheet, and a resource list. Finally, I've included a few lined pages for you to jot down any notes you might want to keep—to-do items, checklists of supplies and comfort measures, lists of who is responsible for what, MealTrain participants, and so on. My wife suggested this addition. She says she would have found a central location to maintain her lists especially helpful during the weeks leading up to my mother's start date.

While I might not be a medical professional, I am a writer intimately acquainted with the VSED process. I also consider myself an activist in the ongoing work to educate people about VSED and to make a dignified death more accessible. My mother's experience galvanized me to advocate for broader end-of-life choices, and I now work with a Western Washington group of VSED advocates— VSED Resources Northwest (VSEDresources.com)—to promote awareness of and access to VSED. Through this advocacy work, I feel like I'm honoring my mother's life more than her death.

Although, to be honest, I'm trying to do that, too.

"You know," I told my mother a few days before she started VSED, "I'm going to write about this."

"I hope you do," she said, nodding decisively. "I hope my story can help other people."

That's the whole point of this book, really: to help others looking for a peaceful, dignified way out of a long, agonizing death marked by untenable losses. I hope it does its job.

SECTION TIPS

Here is the first set of tips for anyone looking into VSED for themselves or a loved one:

1. Call your local hospice care organization and find out if they already support VSED. If they don't, ask them to help. As my mother always used to say, you don't get what you don't ask for.

2. Hire a death doula and assemble a team of folks who are experienced with VSED and delegate accordingly. Try to include at least one medical professional who can be with you throughout the dying process, especially at the end.

3. Be prepared to do a lot of planning. I mean, A LOT. VSED is a marathon not a sprint and, accordingly, requires significant preparation.

4. Use palliative care medicines as soon as possible in the VSED process to manage the dying person's anxiety, thirst, and hunger.

PREPARING FOR VSED

Stopping eating and drinking might sound simple, but carrying out VSED successfully in a manner that minimizes suffering requires significant preparation. In this section, I'll try to break down the complex preparation process into actionable steps.

In my family's case, we started preparing a couple of years before my mom did VSED. It took several months to educate ourselves about the process and to settle the legal matters involved in hastening one's own death, and then, as our attorney suggested, Mom tried to focus on enjoying the time she had left. That meant attending her grandchildren's soccer practices, games, and school events; spending time with friends and family; reading, birdwatching, and working in her garden; visiting Alaska and Wyoming, her favorite travel destinations; and going for walks with her grandchildren and our family dog, Leila, who Mom loved like her own.

In theory, focusing on daily life sounds straightforward. But in reality, the two years between Mom's VSED decision and her actual VSED start date were filled with ups and downs as her dementia progressed and she and my dad struggled with the ever-present question: When would be the right time for her to stop eating and drinking? They also worried about the legality of VSED—might Dad or I be arrested for helping her die? Our attorney assured us that we wouldn't, but she also told us that there had never been a court case involving VSED before, and neither my dad nor

I wanted to be legal guinea pigs.

My dad was concerned, too, about my mother potentially suffering through days or weeks of dehydration. Like him, Mom wondered if there might be a faster, more humane alternative to dying by VSED, such as a MAID-type drug overdose, but they couldn't figure out a viable way to procure enough medicine to allow Mom to overdose. Even if they had, they decided that active suicide—where someone takes a deliberate action to end their life—felt different from VSED, in which an individual fails to take an action (eating and drinking). My parents didn't want to get anyone in trouble for Mom's decision to hasten her death, and if the overdose didn't work and Mom ended up in a care facility due to a failed suicide attempt, that would only make matters worse.

If only MAID were available to people with Alzheimer's disease, we all agreed. But in order to qualify for Washington State's current MAID law, the patient has to have fewer than six months to live. MAID laws are written in a way to protect those with decreased mobility and cognition, but unfortunately, that means that people like my mother are forced to look elsewhere to escape dementia's brutal end stages.

These conversations about Mom's impending death were almost always tense and painful, and they never seemed to be resolved. At one point, my father was ready to give up and look at memory care facilities. But when he suggested this might be the best course of action, my mother became enraged and vowed she would kill herself before she would ever allow herself to be institutionalized. I, for one, believed her, and Dad must have too because he took memory care off the table. Finally, in October 2019, they closed in on a start date: late January 2020. That way, Mom could enjoy one last holiday season. With her start date in sight, Mom settled into a less agitated state, calmer and more at peace

15

than I had seen her in years. Her dementia even seemed to improve slightly as, at last, the end to her suffering was in sight.

In the pages ahead, I'll describe the steps to take while preparing for VSED, grouped in sequential order when possible. For more details about when to take each step, refer to the "VSED Timeline" section near the end of the book.

THE DECISION

It may seem obvious, but the first step in the VSED process is deciding to do VSED. In general, VSED requires considerable strength of will and is best suited to independent individuals who have both a team to support them and the ability to withstand days or weeks without food and water. Choosing VSED is a personal decision; that said, this book is intended for people who have been diagnosed with a degenerative disease or other terminal condition that renders them unable to qualify for medical aid in dying (MAID), or for individuals who are terminally ill and reside in a region where medical aid in dying isn't available. If you are not terminally ill, I strongly suggest that you talk to your medical team about holistic care to treat your physical symptoms and seek out a mental health professional to treat any emotional suffering before you decide to end your life.

Any end-of-life decision-making process should include conversations with loved ones, an attorney, and at least one trusted medical professional. Not everyone will be okay with a voluntary early exit from suffering. If dysfunction exists within your family, don't expect it to magically disappear at the end of your life. As our Hospice nursing manager told us, "Families experience death the same way they experience life." For this reason, family members should be allowed to participate or not according to their comfort level, and details about your VSED start date and location should only be shared with supportive family members and friends.

In our case, a close family member tried at the last minute to keep Mom from carrying out her VSED plan. My parents ended up preventing this family member from taking part in Mom's end-of-life process, and the resulting family fracture was incredibly painful. Two years later, it still is, if I'm being honest. But Mom, determined to end her life on her own terms, stayed the course—with the rest of us beside her every step of the way.

WHEN TO START

Once you've made the decision to commit to VSED, the next step is determining when you will stop eating and drinking. For those with a progressive physical ailment, there are often clear markers, such as a loss of function requiring institutionalization or a level of pain or other aspect of disease progression that makes continued existence untenable. For those with dementia, the issue of when to start is more complicated—just as the rest of the VSED process can be. But for many dementia sufferers, VSED is the only legal option to escape a long, slow, tortuous death.

Deciding when to start was definitely the hardest part of the planning process for my family, and it led to many difficult conversations as well as a few painful confrontations. When is the right time to go? What if you miss your "window" of competency and capability? How do you know if you've already missed it? The answers to these questions are unique to each individual. For Mom, the paranoia that accompanied her dementia made it difficult for her to trust that the people around her had her best interests at heart, which led to tears, shouting, and strained relationships.

After numerous conversations and several heated arguments among various family members, my mother came up with three markers, or potential roadblocks to her continued existence with Alzheimer's disease. She didn't want to live if (1) she couldn't physically take care of herself (i.e., shower and use the toilet without help); OR (2) she couldn't recognize her friends and family members; OR (3) she could no longer live safely at home with my father, her husband of 55 years. When that third non-negotiable became a reality due to her increasing agitation and aggression, she opted to do VSED rather than move to a memory care facility.

WHERE TO DIE

Another major decision is choosing a home base for VSED. Some care facilities refuse to allow VSED on their premises due to liability or for religious/philosophical reasons. In that case, if you are a current resident of a care facility, you might need to rent a vacation home, move in with a family member, or even rent an RV and park it at a relative's house for the duration of the VSED process.

My mother was lucky. She had my dad to look after her, and they owned a condo not far from my house that offered autonomy, lovely views, and kind neighbors. When they heard she was on hospice, two of her and Dad's neighbors came by to sit with her for a while, and others reached out to Dad to see if they could help. Another benefit of having hospice care involved—by having the dying process officially sanctioned, you end up being able to talk to people outside your trusted circle about your impending death, and even, maybe, say goodbye. Not only that, but your surviving family members are embraced by the community in a way they might not otherwise experience.

DOCUMENTATION

VSED Videos

Video recordings are helpful to document your decision. You should plan to record two videos before carrying out VSED. One should feature a longer discussion of why you're choosing to hasten your death, while in the other, speak directly to yourself about why you need to keep going with VSED, even if you want to quit. The long video is a record of your decision in your own words and can be useful if anyone questions your decision-making capacity. The shorter video is for the VSED process, intended to help you through the often-difficult middle stages before unconsciousness sets in.

At the suggestion of our attorney, we recorded both of these videos. In the longer one, which we recorded at the time Mom decided she was interested in VSED, I interviewed Mom about her reasons for wanting to avoid the late stages of dementia, prompting her with questions about her family's history with Alzheimer's. She was still in the early stages of her disease when we recorded the video and was able to talk at length about her reasons for choosing VSED. Not only was this helpful from a legal point, but I've found that watching my mom talk in clear terms about her choice to hasten her death has helped me remember why she made the decision to forego some good days to avoid bad years.

Also, it's just nice to have a video of an in-depth conversation with her while she was still cognitively sound. So many of my family videos that feature her are basically snippets of fun—decorating holiday cookies, hanging ornaments on the Christmas tree, watching the kids' soccer games on Saturday mornings. But more of my time with my mom over the past five decades was spent talking about the big things in life; I'm glad I captured one of those conversations on film.

The second video we recorded was shorter—about a minute and a half—and featured Jane encouraging herself to stay the course during VSED even if the going got tough. The attorney suggested Mom record this video because people who do VSED tend to experience delirium after several days of dehydration and can become agitated and confused. We were glad to have this recommendation when, during the middle stages, Mom became agitated trying to remember why she was doing VSED. Her sister pulled up the short video on her phone, and Mom settled down after listening to herself a few times through and being reminded that she had chosen VSED to avoid going into memory care. While she experienced moments of confusion at other points in the process, that day was the only time she became agitated about VSED itself.

That's another tip: Make sure that you have the short video available on multiple devices and that everyone on the care team knows how to access it if needed. For us, it was an incredibly useful tool to combat confusion in the middle to late stages of VSED.

POLST (Portable Orders for Life-Sustaining Treatment)

Soon after deciding to do VSED, you'll want to specify your wishes on a POLST to not be resuscitated, and ask your doctor to sign it. This is also a good time to discuss issues of decision-making capacity with your physician, especially if you are experiencing cognitive decline, and to talk to your doctor about your decision to do VSED.

Durable Power of Attorney for Healthcare (DPAHC)

Before beginning VSED, you'll want to choose a durable power of attorney for healthcare, if you haven't already. This is the person who will make medical decisions for you should you become incapacitated. Be sure to choose someone who is supportive of your VSED choice. In our family's case, my father was my mother's DPAHC, and I was the alternate agent in case Dad was unable to make decisions.

Advance Care Directives and VSED Statement

Directives from organizations like the Alzheimer's Association allow you to document your end-of-life wishes in great detail, which is a helpful way to protect your right to choose VSED. You may also opt to attach a supplemental statement explaining why you are choosing to hasten your death.

Two years before Mom did VSED, she and Dad worked with their attorney and a death doula to fill out several directives, including one from End of Life Washington and one from the Alzheimer's Association. Mom also crafted a supplemental VSED statement that detailed her dementia diagnosis and her objections to institutionalized care (see Appendix C). She then signed her directives, had them notarized, and added a copy—along with copies of her POLST and DPAHC—to a three-ring binder we referred to as Mom's "VSED packet." We also made sure to save electronic copies on the cloud.

Here's another tip: Make extra copies of your VSED packet and share them with your legal and medical teams.

Release of Liability Forms

Shortly before you begin VSED, ask your attorney to draw up documents that release liability for anyone and everyone who might be involved in helping you hasten your death. Also, discuss issues of decision-making capacity with your attorney in advance, particularly if you are declining cognitively.

In our case, Mom met with her attorney, Erin, regularly over a period of several years, each time reaffirming her decision to do VSED. This established solid documentation of her end-of-life wishes while providing evidence to the rest of us of Jane's stalwart commitment to VSED. The last time we met with Erin was the week before Mom started VSED, at which time we provided the list of paid caregivers and attending family members who had requested a signed Release of Liability form to help Mom with VSED. The signed forms were then placed in the binder that held the rest of Mom's VSED packet.

When the time came for Mom to start VSED, the binder was placed in an easily accessible location in case Adult Protective Services decided to investigate Mom's dying process as possible elder abuse. That didn't happen to us, but it did happen to another family in our area. Fortunately, their VSED packet convinced Adult Protective Services that the decision to do VSED was solely the dying person's, and their process continued without further intervention.

HOSPICE CARE SUPPORT

A supportive doctor you've shared your plans with should be willing to make a hospice care referral. Alternately, you can contact a local or regional hospice care facility or organization and ask them to support your choice to stop eating and drinking. If they won't support the beginning of the process because you don't have an immediately terminal diagnosis, ask them to come in midway when either you are actively dying, you are comatose, or you qualify for a diagnosis of Failure to Thrive.

My mother's doctor suggested we talk to our local hospice care facility a few months before she stopped eating and drinking, and we were both surprised and encouraged when they agreed to come on board once she was "mostly sleeping." They were helpful in many ways, not least of which was alleviating family and caregiver concerns about being held legally responsible for Mom's choice to hasten her death. We called Hospice when she died, and they handled the death certificate/reporting requirements for us. They also offered support through at-home nurse visits, sessions with a social worker, grief counseling for the surviving family, and spiritual support before, during, and after VSED.

The day my mom died, a Hospice chaplain sat with Dad, Mom's sister Charlotte, and me in the room where Mom was in a coma, asking each of us to share her life story from our individual perspectives. It was an incredibly meaningful way to spend Mom's final day: celebrating who she had been across the seven and a half decades of her life. An hour after the chaplain left, Mom slipped away, and to me it felt as if she were saying, *"Yes, that's who I was, and now I'm ready to go."*

MEDICAL SUPPORT

If Hospice accepts you into their program before you start VSED, they typically have a physician on staff who can prescribe the palliative medicines that limit suffering and enable a peaceful dying process. But if you aren't accepted into Hospice, or they only agree to come on board in the middle stages of VSED (like with my mom), then you'll need to find someone else to write prescriptions to manage anxiety, pain, and delirium.

Unfortunately, while stopping eating and drinking is not illegal, many physicians are reluctant to discuss VSED as an end-of-life choice. As of the writing of this book—February 2022—it can be a challenge to find a physician who will support a patient's VSED choice and, importantly, prescribe the necessary medications. Nurses and nurse practitioners are more accustomed to creating end-of-life care plans for their patients, and these plans are often workable for those who choose VSED. But without official clinical guidelines on how to assist a patient who stops eating and drinking, many medical professionals in the United States are reluctant to become involved.

The VSED Resources Northwest (VRNW) website offers several resources to help you obtain medical support. If your doctor has questions about VSED, you can refer them to the one-page "FAQ for Physicians" on VSEDresources.com for more information about the process, its symptom burden, and a clinician's responsibility when a patient chooses VSED. The VRNW website also has a link to a video recording of a May 2021 webinar for medical providers hosted by the Palliative Care Institute at Western Washington University—basically, a VSED 101 course for medical professionals. If your physician, nurse practitioner, or physician's assistant is reluctant to support your decision, you might suggest they watch this webinar. If they are still reluctant, ask them to refer you to a physician or nurse practitioner who will support your choice. Again, VSED isn't illegal, which means you have the right to hasten your death—and the right to have your wishes honored by your health care provider.

For Mom's VSED process, we lined up a supportive nurse practitioner early on in 2017, but he backed out in 2019 only a few months before Mom's start date. No one else was willing to prescribe Mom's palliative meds on such short notice, so her only option was to ask her doctor at the local senior health clinic, part of a Catholic healthcare system that is decidedly against hastening one's own death. When she asked him to write the prescriptions, Mom's doctor was initially resistant because, he said, he didn't have any knowledge of or experience with the process of stopping eating and drinking. But Mom kept asking him to support her choice, and eventually he agreed to prescribe the medicines she would need to remain comfortable during VSED. She had been resolute about her end-of-life wishes for a long time, he said, which gave him confidence that she wasn't making the decision to hasten her death lightly.

I'm so thankful he changed his mind. If he hadn't, I have little doubt that my mother would have sought out a more direct, possibly even violent means of ending her life.

Because palliative care meds are essential to minimize suffering during VSED, here's another tip: Have a conversation with your doctor early on about your end-of-life choices. This might mean you'll have an ally in your corner if and when you decide to stop eating and drinking, and either way, you'll know where your doctor stands well in advance. Also, someone other than a physician may be able to write your VSED prescriptions. Check with your state's department of health to find out who is approved to write prescriptions in your area.

DEATH DOULA

While Mom's physician provided the all-important palliative care prescriptions, Dad and I both believe that Mom's peaceful passing was possible because we had the assistance of an amazing death doula. We were lucky to receive a referral from Erin, our attorney, to Nancy, a former maternal child public health nurse and birth doula who turned to death doula work after taking care of her parents at the end of their lives. Nancy, her doula partner Andrea, and their caregiving team took charge of Mom's medication, comfort measures, and more as they shepherded all of us compassionately through the last days of Mom's life. Without them, I seriously doubt that Mom's passing would have been considered a good death. We will forever be grateful to the assistance that Nancy, Andrea, Beth, and Joan offered during the long days and nights that we sat vigil at

Mom's bedside.

This is one of the most important pieces of advice I can share: Whatever you do, please don't attempt VSED without adequate medical support and palliative care. That's how VSED horror stories happen. It truly takes a team to make sure the patient remains comfortable while dying from dehydration. As a former nurse and current death doula, Nancy was the ideal candidate to help us make sure Mom remained free from pain and suffering.

To find a doula, do an online search in your area or check out directories at organizations like the National End-of-Life Doula Alliance (NEDA) or International End of Life Doula Association (INELDA). When you interview a potential match, ask them if they have VSED experience. If they don't, you might consider referring them to VSEDresources.com to find out about online presentations and training sessions for death doulas interested in learning how to support people who choose VSED.

PAID CAREGIVERS

Hospice nurses typically only check in occasionally; they aren't on site 24/7 as I mistakenly believed before my mother's death, so if you want nursing care on site, you'll have to hire professional caregivers. However, finding caregivers to help with VSED can also be challenging. Like care facilities, many care agencies won't allow their employees to support VSED (again, for liability or religious/philosophical reasons). Private caregivers are a better choice, but you should find those who are experienced with VSED or at least willing to support a VSED death, which might be difficult. A death doula may be able to provide referrals to experienced VSED caregivers they've worked with in the past—another reason to hire one.

For everyone's sake, be sure to interview any potential

caregiver in person and determine where they stand on an individual's right to hasten their own death via VSED. Also, talk about timing and availability. To avoid any interruption in care, you'll need caregivers who are willing to provide a two-week commitment. This means you should have a specific start date in mind before interviewing members of your caregiving team. Having a death doula and paid caregivers—typically LPNs or CNAs—who have committed to being on site throughout the dying process allows family members to be present mostly as emotional support.

Nancy, our death doula, found professional caregivers for us (among other vital tasks) and created a 24/7 coverage schedule at our request beginning on day three. No one in our immediate family had any medical training or experience, and we were worried about Mom suffering from dehydration, so we wanted comprehensive nursing coverage. However, that can be an expensive choice, so if you don't want or need 24/7 care, you can certainly get by with less help, particularly during the early and middle stages of VSED.

VSED SUPPLIES

As previously mentioned, dying from dehydration can be intensely uncomfortable, especially if you're not prepared. In the week leading up to VSED, you'll want to stock up on the supplies listed below. If you're working with Hospice, they can help you procure some of these items, and they might even bill Medicare for part or all of the rental cost of the hospital bed, bedside commode, and certain other supplies. Otherwise, ask your doctor or death doula where to find the items below.

The website VSEDresources.com lists additional supplies, but these were the ones my family found most useful:

- Hospital bed (rental)
- Bedside commode (rental)
- Walker (rental)
- Shower bench
- Cool-air humidifier
- Waterproof sheets for the hospital bed
- Incontinence products
- Lip balm (non-petroleum)
- Oral foam swabs
- Lotion
- Atomizer spray bottles (for misting dry mouth and lips)
- Plastic syringes to administer liquid palliative care medication

COMFORT MEASURES

The physical space where you'll be during the VSED process needs to be prepared in advance, too. Some questions to think about include whether or not you want the room where you are dying to be cool or warm; what kind of music you would like to have playing, if any; and what books you might like to have read to you at different stages of the dying process. Do you want flowers, candles, potted plants, or incense in the room where you are dying? What kind of atmosphere would you like in your home in general—quiet and contemplative? A celebration of your lived experience? Regular life continuing on? Do you want visitors, and if so, at what point do you want the visits from all but your closest loved ones to stop?

Here are a few measures my family found especially meaningful:

- Cuddling in bed
- Enjoying the view from the window
- Arranging pictures of cherished people
- Watching favorite movies
- Sharing memories
- Curating a playlist of favorite music
- Sitting quietly in a rocking chair
- Snuggling with a favorite pet
- Dressing in comfy clothing
- Hearing and retelling family stories

VSEDresources.com also has a comprehensive list of comfort measures to help you prepare in advance. You might consider downloading this list in the week before VSED and sitting down with a family member to talk about what appeals to you. Sharing your comfort wishes with a loved one can offer a reassuring first step into what is likely to be a physically and emotionally intense ten- to fourteen-day journey.

SAYING GOODBYE

Before you start VSED, consider celebrating with your loved ones. In non-pandemic times, you might consider throwing a party and inviting friends and family from near and far to attend—a sort of living funeral, as it were. Or, if you prefer something more low-key, reach out to the important people in your life one by one. Saying goodbye allows you and your loved ones closure and can contribute to both a more peaceful leave-taking and a less fraught grieving process.

In our family's case, relatives and friends traveled from all over the country to see Mom in the months before she started VSED, while others called and wrote letters. This was one of the most meaningful parts of the experience because Mom got to connect deeply with and say heartfelt goodbyes to almost everyone she loved. The timing of her death—only a month before the COVID-19 pandemic started—highlighted just what a privilege that would turn out to be.

AFTER-DEATH PLANS

Defining your choices for directly after death can help your family members and loved ones in VSED's immediate aftermath. Would you like any religious or spiritual rites performed before or after your death? Would you like your death acknowledged in any special way, such as lighting a candle, reading a poem, or singing a song? Which do you want: to be buried or cremated? Would your family like to spend time washing your body and dressing you in the clothes you will be buried or cremated in? How soon after your death do you want your body removed from your home or the place you chose to die? Do you want a funeral or memorial service? If so, when and where?

Again, these are questions a death doula can help you sort out.

My mother chose cremation and set it up well in advance of VSED. Our Hospice social worker provided a packet of lavender salts, and soon after Mom died, our death doula led us in a ritual cleansing of Mom's hands and feet during which we ruminated on everything her hands had held and everywhere her feet had ventured in the course of her 75 years of life. We also lit a candle, read poems that we had picked out ahead of time, and sang a song of celebration. It was a beautiful, moving ritual, and it helped those of us who were present transition to a new stage of grief.

FINAL VSED PREP

You've made the decision to do VSED, picked the place where you will die, and picked a start date. You've talked to your loved ones, gotten your legal paperwork in order, and identified hospice, medical, and caregiver support. You know who will be with you every step of the way. If it isn't long before your start date now, and you've stocked up on VSED supplies and made lists of possible comfort measures that might alleviate some of the discomforts of dying, then you're ready for your final VSED prep.

ARRANGE ROOM WHERE YOU PLAN TO DIE

My mother essentially nested, placing the hospital bed where she would have the best view of the lake in the distance and moving in a bookcase with her favorite books and framed photos that she could see from her bed. She left her bulletin board of favorite photos, political cartoons, and humorous/inspiring quotes in place above her hospital bed, and that became a sort of touchstone for the rest of us, a reminder of who she was and why she didn't want to live any longer with Alzheimer's. We also moved an adjustable floor lamp and a gliding rocker—the one my wife and I rocked our twins to sleep in when they were little—into the room so that caregivers and family members could sit beside Mom's bed and talk to her, read to her, or sing to her. The low lighting and warm intimacy of the room made it feel like a safe cocoon from the rest of the world where we could focus on one thing: helping Mom transition from this life to whatever comes next.

REDUCE CALORIES AND CLEANSE COLON

This step isn't absolutely required, but some people choose to reduce their calories in the weeks before VSED and to cleanse their bowels a few days ahead of time with a colonoscopy prep prescribed by their medical team. My mother significantly reduced her sugar intake in the week before her start date, and she did a colon cleanse the day she stopped eating, which was two days before she stopped drinking. This prep meant she experienced zero gastrointestinal issues during her ten-day VSED process despite a lifelong struggle with GI tract issues.

SCHEDULE FINAL CHECK WITH ATTORNEY

Confirm your decision-making capacity, especially if you have cognitive decline. Obtain signed liability documents absolving anyone who is planning to help of legal responsibility for your death.

TALK TO DOCTOR ABOUT MEDICATIONS

Some medications for chronic issues might have disadvantages that outweigh their benefits at the end of life, and others might interact negatively with palliative care prescriptions.

PICK UP PALLIATIVE CARE MEDICINES

Obtain medicines in advance to make sure your pharmacy has them available and you have them before you start. Be sure to specify that medications should come in liquid or sublingual form (designed to be placed onto or under the tongue, where the medication dissolves and is absorbed rapidly into the bloodstream). Sipping even a little bit of water to wash down a pill can prolong the VSED process. Also, have the full amounts of the medications you'll need. You don't want to run out in the middle of the process and have to scramble to get another prescription filled.

TEST ANTI-ANXIETY MEDS AHEAD OF TIME

Some people's body chemistry responds differently to anti-anxiety medication. You'll want to know in advance if a prescription is going to make you more agitated rather than help allay your anxiety over the dying process.

PRACTICE MOUTH CARE

Before VSED begins, family members should practice swabbing out the patient's mouth with foam sponge sticks, using the atomizer spray bottle, and assessing the dryness of the patient's lips and nose. Your doula, an experienced VSED caregiver, or a hospice care nurse should be able to coach you on these techniques.

DECIDE WHO WILL ADMINISTER MEDICINES

In our case, the family asked our doula and paid caregivers to administer Mom's medication during VSED. As none of us had any medical experience, we felt better having professionals in charge of the meds. If you decide to have family members administer your medication, talk to your doula or one of your paid caregivers about how and when to administer doses, and consider practicing ahead of time.

CREATE LOGBOOK TO TRACK MEDS & HOURS

Our doula maintained careful records in a binder that lived on the kitchen counter (along with Mom's VSED packet) throughout the VSED process, from tracking medication doses to the scheduling of paid caregiver shifts. She also kept detailed notes of daily events in the logbook, and afterward gave us a copy of her notes to keep as a record of Mom's final days.

RECORD A SHORT, MOTIVATIONAL VIDEO

If you haven't already done so, speak to yourself on camera. Explain your commitment to and reasons for doing VSED, and encourage yourself to keep going if the going gets tough. Keep it short and to the point. As previously mentioned, this video can be useful if someone calls the authorities to intervene, or you become delirious from dehydration. Assign one person to share the video with you, someone you trust implicitly and have known a long time. My mother's sister was our point person because despite a decade of dementia, Mom still knew her every time. When Mom became agitated from dehydration during the middle stages of VSED, her sister showed her the shorter video she'd recorded, and it reassured Mom that stopping eating and drinking was, indeed, her choice and no one else's.

MEET WITH CAREGIVERS & FAMILY MEMBERS

Discuss how to handle medication and requests for food and water. This is especially important when cognitive decline is involved. Our paid caregivers agreed ahead of time to contact a family member or the doula if Mom asked for food or water. This ensured that the caregivers wouldn't be placed in the difficult position of having to refuse a dying woman's requests for sustenance. Mom informed us that if she were to ask for food or water during the process, we should remind her that if she stopped VSED, she would have to go into memory care. This strategy was effective because even in the early stages of the process, my mother didn't always remember that she had chosen to start VSED, thanks to the damage to her short-term memory from a decade of living with dementia. It also reassured those of us charged with helping her that she was still resolute because if she'd really wanted to, she could have stopped VSED at any time in the first four or five days.

REMOVE FOOD FROM THE RESIDENCE

Clean food surfaces thoroughly, too. The home should remain free of food and food smells until the patient is no longer mobile, so plan accordingly. In our case, the necessity of removing all food became abundantly clear on the second night of VSED when Mom, in the throes of sundowning, forgot she wasn't supposed to eat and helped herself to a pan of lasagna that was out on the kitchen counter. Fortunately, she only managed to lick the serving spoon a couple of times before a family member noticed and reminded her that she had stopped eating and drinking. At that point, we moved any remaining food in the condo to my house, which was only a couple of miles away.

ORGANIZE COMMUNITY SUPPORT

Ask for help from trusted friends; your loved ones are going to need it. We asked a friend to set up a MealTrain—an online service where people sign up to deliver meals on specific dates—and invited people who wanted to support our family while Mom was "on hospice," as we publicly referred to it, to participate. That way, we didn't have to worry about meal preparation while actively supporting Mom's dying process, and our community had a tangible way to express their love and support. We asked participants to bring meals to my house, since my parents' condo was food-free, and we also let them know not to expect personal interactions in order to protect the privacy and intimacy of VSED.

MARK THE BEGINNING WITH YOUR TEAM

The day before you start VSED, bring the entire team (family members and caregivers) together to ensure that everyone is on the same page. Describing your reasons for choosing VSED and reaffirming your commitment to hastening your death can be reassuring—and inspiring—to those who have agreed to help you die. The night before my mother's VSED process began, our death doula gathered all supporting family members and paid caregivers together at my parents' condo. There, she told a story that illustrated the similarities between birth and death and led all of us in songs of celebration of Mom's life and, especially, her strength. It was an incredibly moving ceremony, and it set a positive tone for the next ten difficult, emotional days.

STOPPING EATING AND DRINKING

Now that you've read through the suggestions for planning and preparing for VSED, I'll try to give you an idea of what to expect from the different phases of VSED. For family members and caregivers, I'll include a description of the symptoms the patient is likely to experience and what treatment steps you can take to minimize suffering. I'll also share glimpses into what my mother and those of us who watched over her experienced in each stage of VSED.

Voluntarily stopping eating and drinking typically involves three phases: (1) *early stage*, during which the patient is alert, occasionally hungry, often thirsty, and still able to interact with the world around them; (2) *middle stage,* when the patient experiences progressive weakness, confusion, and an increased need for sleep as their body begins to break down; and (3) *late or dying stage*, during which the patient is mostly unresponsive as they reach the end stages of dehydration. For people who choose VSED, the end stages of the dying process are similar to what many dying patients on traditional hospice experience.

The duration of these three phases can vary greatly. For some seriously ill patients who are already weak when they start the process, VSED can take as few as four or five days. For my mother and people like her—physically robust but cognitively impaired—the process typically takes longer. For healthier people, the average time from cessation of drinking to death is ten to fourteen days. But if the patient consumes even a small amount of water during the early and middle phases, the process can be prolonged by days or weeks, thereby drawing out the suffering of everyone involved.

Much of this section of the book will be directed at family members and caregivers who carry the heaviest load of ensuring the patient achieves their desired outcome. And make no mistake—helping a loved one complete VSED is a heavy load, both physically and emotionally. VSED can be gut-wrenching for families, which is why it's so important to have a medical team that is experienced with VSED. I don't regret helping Mom stop eating and drinking, but I often wish I wouldn't have had to. A friend who assisted her father's VSED process refers to it as an "over-ask," a term that resonates with me. This is true especially for people with cognitive decline who choose VSED—and yet another reason why it's crucial that the dementia patient be able to consistently articulate their wishes to their family and caregiving team at the time they choose to stop eating and drinking.

Perhaps understandably, VSED is less complicated for people who have a disease other than dementia. Without memory loss and cognition issues, stopping eating and drinking is often more straightforward. Not only is there no question of capacity to potentially wrestle over with unsupportive family members (more on that later in the book), but the patient typically doesn't become confused or agitated until the middle stages of dying, when their organs begin to fail and their cognitive processes begin to break down. Dementia complicates VSED for patient and family members alike, as my family certainly discovered.

If medical aid in dying had been available to people suffering from Alzheimer's disease, I think my mom would have opted to use it, and perhaps some of us who assisted her VSED process wouldn't now live with the guilt of helping her die. Mom was very clear that VSED was her decision, and yet I still had to redirect her requests for food and water when she would forget what she was doing. I still had to remind her that she had chosen to die rather than go into a memory care facility, and that role for me was painful. I knew that I could have brought her ginger ale or ice cream when she forgot about her decision to stop eating and drinking, and she would have stayed alive. Against her wishes and miserable, perhaps, but alive—at least temporarily. Again, I have no doubt she would have tried to find a different, much more traumatizing way to die if VSED hadn't been available; that knowledge helped me stay the course during her dying process.

On the other hand, if Mom *had* qualified for medical aid in dying or gone a different, more direct route, she would have been gone in a matter of minutes or hours, and Dad, Mom's sister Charlotte, and I never would have experienced the days of snuggling, talking, singing, and deep connection with Mom that VSED allowed us to share as her body slowly shut down. I'm grateful for the time I shared with my mom as she lay dying even as I sometimes wish I hadn't been so intimately involved in her death.

VSED is complex, especially for the loved ones of those who choose to die this way.

Because VSED takes an average of ten to fourteen days, the patient has the time and ability to change their mind early on in the process. But in the middle stages, the patient's dying process reaches the point of no return. At that point, even if they were to try to stop VSED, their body would be too far into organ failure from sustained dehydration to recover. In the VSED literature, I've read of cases where the patient vacillated too late or became delirious and fought against dying, which was painful for everyone involved. In some of these cases, palliative sedation may have been indicated given that the patient was past the point of recovery.

Palliative medications for VSED typically target anxiety,

pain, and delirium/agitation. Before Mom stopped eating and drinking, the friend who coined the term "over-ask" recommended we read through the Royal Dutch Medical Association's online guide titled "VSED: Caring for people who consciously choose not to eat and drink." (See the Resource List at the end of this book for more information.) After perusing the medication section of the guide, we asked Mom's physician to prescribe morphine for pain, haloperidol for delirium and agitation, and lorazepam for anxiety, all in liquid or sublingual form. Mom used each of these medications from the second day onward, and they made a huge impact on her quality of death. She wanted to stay conscious for as long as possible, so the doses started out small. For her, even a small amount of medication was effective in treating her anxiety, dementia-related agitation, and physical discomfort in the early stages.

That's another tip: Don't be afraid to use the palliative medications whenever they may seem necessary. We were afraid of giving Mom too much medication, but when Hospice came on board midway through her VSED process—once she was past the point of recovery—they immediately upped the dosages, and the palliative care medicine allowed her to settle back into the labor of dying.

EARLY PHASE

Timing: 1-4 days on average

Possible complaints: Thirst; hunger; dry mouth, nose, and throat

Treatment: Mouth care; medication for anxiety and (especially for dementia patients) confusion or agitation; a cool-air humidifier placed close to the patient's head

During the first few days of VSED, the patient remains awake and alert and also is typically at their thirstiest. Hunger is usually less of a factor, but people with unaddressed addictions (nicotine, alcohol, drugs, or sugar, even) will likely experience higher levels of discomfort and might even go through withdrawal. It's vital that the patient cut back on anything they routinely crave before starting VSED; otherwise, those cravings could disrupt the VSED process.

The early days of the process provide opportunity for connection and celebration of the patient's life, although some might choose quiet reflection. Whatever works and keeps the patient distracted from their physical discomfort should be pursued. In our case, my mom stopped eating on a Wednesday and took her last drink of water on a Friday. On Saturday, she and I went for a walk around her neighborhood and sat on the couch talking for hours before the entire family piled into two cars and made our way to a favorite park on Puget Sound, where we walked together while my young kids orbited us, running the paved path and climbing boulders at the edge of the marina's jetty. It was a cold, sunny day, the first of February, and at the end of our walk, my mother stood at water's edge between her sister and my dad, all of us sharing the last sunset of her life in what was a simultaneously painful and joyous moment of celebration and sorrow.

By Sunday (technically day two of VSED but day four without food), she was beginning to feel fatigued and light-headed. We stayed closer to home, watching nature documentaries and favorite movies—*Fried Green Tomatoes* and *The Man from Snowy River*—and visiting briefly with my kids and in-laws. Mom talked to her older sister Margaret, whose health didn't allow her to be present for VSED, on the phone most days throughout the early stages, and other family and friends reached out as well. Mom decided to start sleeping in her hospital bed that night, the third night of VSED. Her strength was already starting to give out after four days without food, and her physical boundaries slowly narrowed as she closed in on herself and began the active work of dying.

She didn't complain of hunger in the early days of VSED, but she was thirsty. At first, she could walk to the bathroom and rinse out her mouth, careful to spit out all traces of water. Later, as she weakened, we helped her manage her thirst, using oral foam swabs moistened with water to sponge down her teeth, tongue, and gums; liberally applying a natural, non-petroleum-based lip balm; and occasionally spraying her mouth with fine mist from an atomizer spray bottle. These were the most important comfort measures we could provide, and with low doses of her anti-anxiety meds keeping her calm and relaxed and the humidifier keeping the air in her room from drying out, Mom's thirst was uncomfortable at times but never seemed to reach the point of suffering. Her dementia-related sundowning—confusion and irritability that kicked in late in the day—became worse each day without food and water, and her afternoon agitation required a low dose of haloperidol starting from day two without water onward.

Mom insisted on showering each day of the early phase of VSED, and the prolonged lack of caloric intake combined with low doses of palliative meds exacerbated her existing dementia-related balance issues. Just like I used to do with my babies—and just like Mom used to do with me when I was little—I climbed into the tub beside her and held her up so she wouldn't slip. Those showers are some of my favorite memories from Mom's last week of life—just the two of us in our birthday suits, laughing and talking as she washed her hair and soaped her body and I made sure she didn't fall.

The circular nature of life was everywhere in those early days as my mother transitioned from parent to patient, as I eased from daughter to family caregiver. Our roles—and our relationship—had been complicated by dementia for a while, but over the ten days of VSED, we grew closer. In long talks in her hospital bed with night settling quietly over the condo, I forgave her inevitable failures as a parent and she forgave my occasionally difficult teenage-hood. We snuggled in her bed and talked about the past and the future, about her family history and my kids—our family's future— and I cried on her shoulder at the pain of letting her go while she held me and told me she loved me. The early stage really was a gift, as painful as it was.

As my therapist noted on day six when I called to check in, none of that closeness would have been possible in a hospital or memory care facility. The drawn-out nature of VSED mimics a "natural" death, and in our case, it allowed for a level of communion and connection that made the hard parts more manageable. Yes, there were moments marked by guilt and fear, but there were more moments of love and caring. Knowing that we managed to connect at the end and that my mother escaped the fate she found worse than death—the late stages of Alzheimer's disease—has been a genuine comfort in the two years since she left us.

MIDDLE PHASE

Timing: Varies
Complaints: Thirst; weakness; agitation and/or confusion
Treatments: Mouth care; medication for anxiety, pain, and agitation; help walking or moving in and out of bed

During this phase of VSED, dehydration and caloric deficit can lead to dizziness, weakness, and light-headedness, which means the patient will need more assistance in moving in and out of bed. In our case, the middle stages lasted from day five or so to day eight, when Mom drifted into a coma. There were no more showers after day four, and she began to sleep and dream more of the daylight hours away. She only left her room once during this period—to go out to the living room and watch her beloved hummingbirds flit about the feeders on the back patio. But mostly she lay in her hospital bed with my dog Leila curled up at her feet, sleeping longer and longer as the days passed.

She did ask for soda and ice cream (her favorite sweets) occasionally in the middle stages as dehydration intensified and confusion set in, but after a couple of painful, guilt-inducing episodes of refusing her requests, I started using the phrase we'd discussed ahead of time: "Yes, I can bring you that. But then VSED will end, and you'll have to move into a memory care facility." The threat of being placed into care succeeded every time in reminding her of who she was and what she wanted, and she would immediately rescind her request, usually with a joke of some kind. Then I would ask if I could swab her mouth, use the atomizer spray, and help her apply lip balm, and those steps seemed to alleviate much of her discomfort. The cool-air humidifier also helped as her skin continued to dry out, and the lotion we rubbed into her skin as she slept seemed to keep her comfortable.

This was also the period that was most difficult for her emotionally. When the hospice care nursing manager arrived on day five to meet her before officially signing off on her intake, Mom was crying. When the nursing manager asked what she was upset about, Mom explained that she didn't want to leave her family.

"I'm not afraid to die," she said, characteristically emphatic. She just didn't want to have to say goodbye to my dad, her sisters, my wife and me, her nieces and nephews, her grandchildren. She was ready to go, but leaving us was difficult for her—and for us.

Towards the end of the middle stage, as her organs began to fail, Mom became more confused and agitated during the daylight hours. That's when our Hospice team suggested we up the low doses of palliative medicines. She was past the point of turning back, and keeping her comfortable through the final stages of dying became our primary focus.

LATE PHASE

Timing: 1-4 days on average
Complaints: Agitation; delirium; unconsciousness
Treatments: Medication for anxiety, pain, and agitation; help turning in bed

During the last stage of VSED, the patient falls into a coma. They rarely wake in the final days of the process, their breathing becomes labored and noisy at times, and their mouth hangs open as the body attempts to regulate breathing during unconsciousness. The patient by now is thoroughly dehydrated, and their skin looks thinner, the bones of the face prominent. They no longer look like themselves as they near the threshold of death.

For my mother, the final stage of VSED lasted from day eight to ten. On day eight, I arrived at the condo early and went to see my mother. Beth, the caregiver on early morning duty, told me that Mom hadn't awakened recently, and I wondered if she had finally entered a coma. At the sound of our voices, though, she blinked awake. I sat down at the edge of her bed and took her hand, smiling down at her.

"I'm here, Mom. I'm right here."

She squeezed my hand and gazed up at me with clear eyes full of love, and then she closed her eyes and went back to sleep. She never opened her eyes again.

Later that day, my wife brought our daughters to say their final goodbyes, and we stood around the bed singing tunes from *The Sound of Music*, a favorite we'd watched with my parents on many a movie night since they'd moved to Western Washington five years earlier. Then the kids touched her hand and kissed her cheek before exiting the room to let her sleep on.

The final two days of her life were hard on those of us supporting Mom, and they almost felt longer than the other eight days combined. A few hours after my children said their final goodbyes, Mom's breathing grew labored and her mouth fell open, as if she were trying to suck in as much air as possible. Charlotte, my mother's younger sister, had more experience with sitting with a dying loved one than Dad and I did, and her calm during this period was comforting. Our doula also reassured us that this was a natural stage in the dying process. Mom wasn't suffering, she told us, and this part wouldn't last long.

She was right. By the ninth night, Mom's labored breathing had eased, and we were on a constant death watch.

It was late Monday afternoon—day ten of VSED— when the nurse told me Mom was going. My father, Charlotte, and I had been with her all day, but Mom waited to let go until the three of us stepped out of the room. Dad was in the living room with the kids, getting ready to go outside to watch them ride bikes on the unseasonably warm February afternoon. I would have been with them too, but I'd returned to Mom's room because I'd forgotten my water bottle. Just like me to foil her surprise plan, I could imagine her teasing me. But there would be no more affectionate teasing, no more laughter except in my memories and home videos. She was gone, and I was simultaneously so, so relieved for her and so, so sad for my dad, my aunts and cousins, my wife and me, our kids, and everyone else who loved her.

In the hours after she died, we washed her body and spoke quietly of her life, and then the man from the local crematorium came to wheel her body away on a gurney. My father and father-in-law helped transport her body out of the condo while our doula, my aunt, and I sang a celebratory song of Mom's life, and it was official. VSED was over. Mom was gone, and my grief at losing her inches at a time to a soul-stealing disease became the grief of the motherless adult child—permanent, final, but also better because now I knew for certain that her end wouldn't come in a memory ward where she would suffer inconsolably as a stranger among strangers. I knew now that her death would be peaceful and moving, and that she would leave us with strength and love.

FAST-FORWARDING DEMENTIA

Even before Mom took her last breath, I'd missed her for years. My funny, spirited mother had vanished a little bit more every day, especially in the past year as her dementia had accelerated. I missed my mother as she was when she was younger, when she would fly out to meet me in Seattle and we would travel together throughout Washington, Oregon, and California. I missed hiking with her in Wyoming's Wind River Range, at the Light Tree Preserve in Michigan, in the Cascade Mountains near Seattle. I missed talking about books and writing, about parenting and sisters and relationships. I missed who my mom was before Alzheimer's stole so many memories and connections, leaving us sometimes uncertain how to talk to each other, how to relate without reserve as we used to.

The thing is, she'd been missing herself for years, too. Dementia's curse is that it kills its victims a centimeter at a time, and they're often aware of every loss, every change in personality, every shift in their close relationships. Mom knew exactly what was coming because she'd watched her mother and grandmother die lingering deaths from Alzheimer's disease. That was why she was so convinced that VSED was the best choice both for her—and for the rest of us, too. Thanks to her decision to stop eating and drinking, she died still knowing her husband, her sisters, her children and grandchildren. We won't ever have to visit her in a memory care facility, won't ever be forced to watch her world shrink over the course of months and years, her consciousness slowly narrowing down to a single bed in a single room in a facility she fought bitterly to escape.

And yet, she didn't escape the end stages of Alzheimer's entirely. As I sat at her bedside watching her die, I came to realize that VSED effectively fast-forwarded Mom's dementia, compressing the late stages of Alzheimer's into ten days—ten difficult, emotional days that were the key to escape both for Mom, who didn't want to leave but was ready to go, and for those of us who weren't ready to say goodbye but knew we had to let her go.

VSED was the least bad choice of death for a powerful, willful, funny, intelligent, complex, sometimes difficult person who I loved and fought with, respected and resented, admired and rejected, like many other mothers and daughters who are fortunate enough to share a lifetime together. Despite its challenges, VSED allowed Mom and me to end on a good note, to whittle away all the external noise, to return to a warm, intimate space where I, the daughter, could care for her, the mother, as she crossed over into death, just as she had once cared for me as I crossed over into life.

Planning her death gave Mom time to connect with the important people in her life even as she crafted a peaceful escape from a devastating terminal illness that promised even greater pain and suffering in the years ahead. To pack the final stages of dementia into weeks instead of years was her final gift to herself—and to those of us who loved her. Somehow, my mother knew a good death was possible even with Alzheimer's, and I'm still struck by how wise she was.

SURVIVOR GUILT AND THE
IMPORTANCE OF SELF-CARE

If I could share only one piece of advice for those actively supporting a loved one's VSED process, it would be this: Take care of yourself so that you can help take care of the dying person. Adequate sleep, meals, hydration, and mental health breaks will be difficult to come by during the long days it will take your loved one to die. But just as the process is a marathon for the dying person, it's also a marathon for those who have agreed to support them through their final journey.

If you've experienced a previous loss, you likely know that guilt is a common stage in the grieving process. For survivors of VSED (and I call us that intentionally), the guilt is exacerbated because most of us play what feels like an unusually active role in our loved one's death. Dad and I participated in a VSED support group a year after Mom's death—perhaps the first such support group in the US— and the guilt that participating members felt at being instrumental in our loved ones' deaths was immense. Not insurmountable but definitely significant, and definitely higher than the typical level of guilt someone experiences when a loved one dies. Most of us admitted to sometimes feeling personally responsible for our loved one's death, even though we knew rationally that we weren't.

Another thing group members agreed on was how important self-care—or the lack thereof—had been during the VSED process. In my family's case, our death doula helped us assemble a solid care team for Mom and guided us through every step of the process, which meant I could take a break when things got too difficult emotionally. My aunt offered Mom, her big sister, unwavering support, but she too made sure to take regular breaks from the condo. My father-in-law tried to get my dad to take breaks from Mom's bedside, and he was even occasionally successful. I walked my dogs in the woods every day while meditating or listening to calming music, and the fresh air, quiet time, and exercise fed my brain and soul. I chose to sleep at home and have dinner each night with my family through the first week of Mom's VSED process because staying too long at the condo overwhelmed me emotionally. This practice allowed me to save up enough strength and energy to sleep on my parents' couch during the last few days of the process as my mother lapsed into a coma and neared the end of her life.

Our extended team was important, too. My father-in-law and his partner stayed in the area for several weeks before and after Mom's VSED process, watching the kids, helping out with VSED planning, and spending quality time with my dad and aunt. The MealTrain our friends set up was also incredibly helpful. Not having to worry about where our next meal came from during those tough days was such a gift. And the phone calls and emails from extended family— Mom's older sister, my cousins, our family friends—shored us up for the difficult journey.

On the night my mother fell into her coma, a supermoon rose over the lake at the bottom of the hill below the condo. I walked down to the shore that night and perched on a boulder, gazing out over the beach where my daughters had played since before they could walk. After a while, I meditated in the brilliant moonlight, exhausted from the difficult week, my emotions stretched thinner than I could remember. My mother was leaving, and there was nothing I could do to stop her. Instead, I could only lean on friends and family and try to ride out the waves of grief.

Two years later, I'm still on that grief journey; it seems likely I will be for the rest of my life. Knowing that my mother achieved the good death she wanted surrounded by people who loved her gives me tremendous comfort, though—especially now, when so many elders in care facilities have either been struck down by COVID-19 without a chance to say goodbye or have had to endure months and even years of isolation from loved ones. Mom's fear of dying as a stranger among strangers seems even more prescient now, after two years of watching COVID-19 variants race through our communities, striking down the most vulnerable.

As Mom once said, VSED isn't right for everyone, but it was right for her. I hope this book helps bring this end-of-life choice into reach for more people for whom it is, undeniably, right.

VSED, CAPACITY, AND FAMILY FRACTURE

In this section of the book, I describe the legal basis of VSED, the types of capacity involved in choosing to hasten one's death, and the complications of a dementia diagnosis. I mentioned earlier that a family member tried to challenge Mom's right to carry out VSED; because we aren't the first family to experience such a fracture over an end-of-life decision, I thought it might also be useful to share here what we learned from our experiences with Adult Protective Services and other authorities.

THE QUESTION OF LEGALITY

During the planning period, one of our family's major concerns about VSED was whether or not we could be charged with a crime for helping Mom hasten her death. As our attorney Erin explained, unlike medical aid in dying (MAID), which is recognized by the U.S. Supreme Court and is explicitly authorized in a number of states, VSED is not explicitly authorized by state statute or by court ruling. But that doesn't mean it's illegal. Far from it. The right to refuse *artificial* hydration and nutrition is well-established by the U.S. Supreme Court (more on that below). The right of a person with decision-making capacity to refuse *oral* hydration and nutrition is also presumed legal. While there has yet to be legislation or a court case in the United States that specifically authorizes VSED, there have been no legal challenges to date. Most legal scholars and medical ethicists recognize that any person with decisional capacity has the authority to refuse oral hydration and nutrition, even if such refusal results in death.

One of the most often cited U.S. Supreme Court cases is *Cruzan v. Director, Missouri Department of Health* (1990). Known informally as the first right-to-die case heard by the U.S. Supreme Court, *Cruzan* featured a Missouri family fighting the state for the right to have their daughter Nancy's feeding tube removed. Nancy had been in a persistent vegetative state since a 1983 car accident, but her parents believed she would never have wanted to be kept alive by medical intervention. The state of Missouri argued that without clear evidence of an incompetent patient's wishes, life support in the form of artificial hydration and nutrition should not be removed.

The Supreme Court agreed with the state of Missouri, but—and this is the important part, according to right-to-die advocates—the Court also stated that the Fourteenth Amendment of the U.S. Constitution gives a "competent person" the "right to refuse lifesaving hydration and nutrition." Because of *Cruzan*, right-to-die advocates began a push to popularize the use of advance health directives so that individuals can document their end-of-life medical wishes ahead of time. Advance directives (also known as Health Care Directives and Living Wills) are now a well-established planning tool used across the United States.

TWO TYPES OF CAPACITY

As our attorney Erin patiently explained more than once, there are two types of decision-making capacity that relate to VSED: *testamentary* and *decisional*. Testamentary capacity (and contractual capacity) can be fairly simple to assess. Does the person know who they are, do they know who they are authorizing to make decisions on their behalf, and can they consistently recall and articulate their decision to stop eating and drinking? If the answer is yes, then the individual is capable of signing legal documents to memorialize in writing their intent to end their life via VSED. This is why the dementia patient must give up good days if they choose VSED—if they wait too long and their disease progresses too far, they won't have the testamentary capacity to choose to stop eating and drinking.

Like testamentary capacity, *decisional* capacity—a person's ability to make medical decisions for themselves—does *not* depend on an individual's ability to cook or check email, nor does it hinge on a diagnosis of dementia. Rather, decisional capacity is determined by the patient's ability to not only understand information relevant to a decision but also to appreciate the consequences of their choice. To assess someone's decisional capacity, the evaluator must examine the individual's process of making a decision, not the nature of the result. Research has shown that most individuals in the early stages of dementia are capable of participating in decisions about their course of treatment—and, from an ethical standpoint, should be encouraged to do so.

A social worker at my parents' clinic once told me that nurses and physicians who work with older people assess a patient's mental and physical state during each and every interaction with that patient. At the appointments I attended (and there were a lot in the two years before Mom stopped eating and drinking), my parents' doctor routinely questioned Mom's understanding of what VSED was, her appreciation of the consequences of doing VSED, and her reasons for wanting to hasten her own death. He explained at one of Mom's final visits that he had chosen this method of assessment because Mom had said numerous times that she disliked cognitive testing. Apparently, she had told him shortly after moving to Washington State that she was aware of her mental decline. Quantifying and documenting what she was losing to an incurable, terminal disease, she'd said, felt pointlessly cruel.

When I asked if he thought she should have a mental exam to gauge her medical decision-making capacity, Mom's doctor replied that while such an exam would measure a certain set of data, it wouldn't give a full picture of her capacity to choose and carry out VSED. She'd expressed the same choice, month in and month out, year after year. In his opinion, her consistency of choice was more relevant and meaningful than the results of any cognitive test.

"I've known your end-of-life wishes for a while, Jane," he said. "You've been very clear, and it's all in writing. Unless your wishes have changed?"

"No," she said, as firm as ever. "This is the best decision for me and for my family, and I think it's time to get the show on the road."

FAMILY FRACTURE

Not everyone in the family agreed with this assessment. Karen (not her real name) initially showed support in 2017 when Mom shared her intention to pursue VSED. But in late 2019, only six weeks before the start date my parents had chosen, Karen declared that in her professional opinion as a practicing therapist, Mom had missed her VSED window and no longer had the capacity to make end-of-life decisions for herself. To pursue VSED now, in Karen's opinion, would be "unethical." It was time, she announced, for Mom to move to a memory care facility.

Dad, who was Mom's medical power of attorney, told Karen that he and Mom understood her objections but would be moving forward with VSED anyway. In response, Karen and her husband threatened to report them to Adult Protective Services. Mom and Dad refused to shift, and the conversation ended acrimoniously.

In the weeks that followed, Karen followed through on her threat, and Mom's case became what our attorney Erin called the most "pre-tried" case of VSED she'd witnessed. In the month before Mom stopped eating and drinking, my parents dealt with a welfare check by a sheriff's deputy, who reported them safe and well; a visit from an Adult Protective Services social worker, who determined that they were neither vulnerable adults nor suicidal, as Karen had alleged; and an investigation into Mom's physician by his Catholic employers, who determined that any palliative medications he planned to prescribe were ethically and legally within the scope of care and did not amount to euthanasia, as Karen had charged. The social worker at my parents' geriatric practice also informed us that Karen had called the office in another attempt to intervene in Mom's care, but since my parents hadn't signed a HIPAA release giving Karen access to their medical records, the matter didn't go any further.

Despite the emotional distress that Karen's attempted interventions elicited, our attorney Erin pointed out that the medical group's response, Mom's physician's continued support, and Adult Protective Services' findings were actually quite reassuring.

"These checks are in place to ensure that vulnerable people are protected," Erin wrote in an email after Karen's interventions had finally fizzled out, "and each have concluded that Jane, despite her diagnosis, retains decisional capacity to make her own medical decisions."

Perhaps inadvertently, Karen had paved the way for Mom—and the rest of us—to move forward with VSED free of worry and, perhaps even more importantly to those of us Mom asked to support her choice, with a clear conscience.

And yet, I can't help thinking that we were fortunate. The social worker we were assigned from Adult Protective

Services supported Mom's autonomy and her right to decide what amount of suffering she wasn't willing to live with. But the case could have gone differently if we had been assigned another social worker, or if my parents weren't white, educated, and financially comfortable. We live in a progressive area in a state where medical aid in dying is legal. Our family was extended a privilege that not everyone in the same situation would be given, and even with that privilege, we still felt vulnerable to interference from the authorities.

From subsequent conversations with Mom's hospice care team, I've learned that family fractures like the one we experienced are not uncommon when someone is nearing death because stress and emotions tend to run high at the end of life. The challenge is to keep these emotions from disrupting the dying process, not only for the patient's sake but for the rest of the support team, too.

Ultimately, you can't control how another person will react to your decision to do VSED. As difficult as it might be to accept, not everyone is able to cope with the impending loss of a loved one in a clear and supportive way. Plenty of people believe that VSED is neither right nor ethical, and someone you love and who loves you might actively try to derail your decision to hasten your death. But in the end, as long as you retain decisional capacity, how you die is *your* choice.

The only decision your loved ones get to make is whether or not to support you.

APPENDIX A: ALL THE TIPS

This section is just what the header says—a collection of all the tips from all the chapters, gathered here for easy reference.

1. Call your local hospice care facility and find out if they already support VSED. If they don't, ask them to help. As Jane always said, you don't get what you don't ask for.

2. Find a death doula by conducting an online search in your area or checking out the directories at organizations like National End-of-Life Doula Alliance (NEDA) or International End of Life Doula Association (INELDA). If you can't find a doula with VSED experience, refer them to VSED Resources Northwest (VSEDresources.com) for training.

3. Assemble a team of folks who are experienced with VSED and delegate accordingly. Try to include at least one medical professional who can be with you throughout the dying process, especially at the end.

4. Have a conversation with your doctor early on about your end-of-life choices; that way, you might have an ally in your corner if and when you decide to start VSED. Either way, you'll need a physician to prescribe palliative care medications. If your doctor won't help, ask them to refer you to someone who will.

5. Be prepared to do a lot of planning. I mean, A LOT. VSED is a marathon not a sprint and, accordingly, requires significant preparation.

6. Keep your planning private. Find out early if there are family members who have objections. As difficult as it might be, try to accept that not everyone is able to cope with the impending loss of a loved one in a clear

and supportive way. If you can, try to identify potential fracture points as early as possible to prevent a disruption of the VSED process.

7. Record a video early on in the decision-making process to establish you are choosing VSED of your own free will. A discussion of your reasons for choosing to hasten your death and an understanding of the finality of death that VSED brings might be helpful if your decision to do VSED ends up being challenged.

8. Record a second, shorter video in which you encourage your future self to stay the course. Make sure it's available on multiple devices and that everyone on the care team knows how to access it if needed to combat confusion in later stages of VSED.

9. Paperwork, paperwork, paperwork. Get your papers in order and be sure to leave a clear evidentiary trail detailing your decision to use VSED. This should include a binder that contains copies of a POLST, a DPAHC, a general advance care directive, a statement of intent to do VSED, an advance directive specifically related to Alzheimer's or dementia (if appropriate), and release of liability forms for family members and paid caregivers that an attorney draws up for you no more than a week or two before you commence VSED.

10. Keep the binder accessible throughout the VSED process in case a concerned outsider contacts the authorities. That way, the documents are immediately accessible if needed. More than likely this won't happen, but in the case of the family in our city who was visited by Adult Protective Services *during* VSED, these documents prevented further intervention by the local authorities. Also, make extra copies of your

VSED packet and share them with your legal and medical teams.

11. Pick up palliative care medicines a few days before starting VSED. Also, be sure to obtain all medications in liquid or sublingual (dissolvable under the tongue) form.

12. If you can, test the anti-anxiety medication ahead of time, especially if it's new to you; adjust your prescription as needed.

13. Use palliative care medicines as soon as possible in the VSED process to manage the dying person's anxiety, thirst, and hunger.

14. And lastly, for family members: Take care of yourself so that you can help take care of the person dying by VSED. Just as the VSED process is a marathon for the patient, it's also a marathon for those who have agreed to support the patient through their final journey.

Remember, VSED is a marathon, not a sprint. Teamwork, planning, support, and strength of will can make the dream of a good, peaceful death attainable even in the face of a debilitating terminal condition like dementia.

APPENDIX B: VSED TIMELINE

VSED is unique for everyone who chooses it, and so is finding the right timing. However, once you've set a start date, there are things that should be done at certain intervals, if at all possible. A death doula who is experienced with VSED can help you modify the list below as needed.

SIX OR MORE WEEKS OUT

- Talk to loved ones, your medical team, and your attorney about your decision

- Record your VSED videos—one long and one short

- Complete your VSED packet: POLST, DPAHC, advance directives, and VSED statement

- Request hospice care support

- Find a physician to write palliative care prescriptions

- Find a death doula, preferably one with VSED experience or training

- Determine who among your family and friends will help and what their roles will be

TWO TO FOUR WEEKS OUT

- Choose where to do VSED

- Interview professional caregivers

- Determine what happens to your body after you die

- Organize community support such as a MealTrain

ONE WEEK OUT

- Arrange the room where you will die

- Obtain a hospital bed and other required medical supplies, including palliative care medications

- Have your attorney draw up release of liability forms for family members and paid caregivers

- Test the anti-anxiety medication

- Reduce calories and/or consider colon cleanse

- Meet with caregivers and family members to discuss how to handle medication and requests for food and water

- Remove food from the residence where VSED will take place

- Say your goodbyes to friends and loved ones who won't be part of the VSED process

- Find a meaningful way to mark the coming transition with those who will be supporting you

APPENDIX C: VSED STATEMENT

I thought it might be useful to include the text of my mother's statement of intent to do VSED, which we included in her VSED packet/binder. As you will see, she described her medical history and the loss of independence and decreased quality of life caused by her dementia, and expressly stated that she would be choosing VSED to hasten her death when living was no longer "meaningful." The document was then signed by two non-related witnesses at our attorney's office and, finally, notarized.

~

Supplemental Statement to the Health Care Directive of Jane D. executed on February 1, 2017. This Supplemental Statement is made this 10th day of April in the year 2017.

I, Jane D., having the capacity to make health care decisions, do willfully and voluntarily make this statement to supplement the Health Care Directive I previously executed on 2/1/17. I do so to ensure that my dying shall not be artificially prolonged and to further articulate my unequivocal desire to hasten my death. I intend to utilize the method of VSED (Voluntary Stopping Eating and Drinking) to expedite my death when living is no longer meaningful for me. I do this with the full support of my family.

I do hereby declare that:

In 2010, I was diagnosed with Mild Cognitive Impairment (MCI). With a family history of Alzheimer's on my mother's side—my grandmother, mother, and brother all suffered from this disease—I understood that a diagnosis of MCI was likely the first step toward Alzheimer's. At that point, I decided to continue living a full and adventurous life as long as possible.

In my seven-plus decades on this planet, I've climbed mountains, kayaked wilderness rivers and creeks, cross-country skied miles of trails in the Midwest and in the Rocky Mountains, lived on a historic ranch in the Wind River Mountains, written for numerous publications, and advocated for American women's equality. I have marched on Washington, D.C., numerous times to raise awareness of gender and racial equality, and I co-chaired a group that secured financial assistance for women striving to return to college. With my husband, I also raised two strong, independent, and successful daughters, and have enjoyed watching my grandchildren grow from infants to school-aged children.

After a lifetime of outdoor adventure and intellectual curiosity, and after serving as a teacher and activist in a variety of social settings, I find that my life since the onset of dementia has been significantly diminished. The scope of my life has narrowed dramatically. My dementia has robbed me of my confidence and the wherewithal to engage in both my local and broader community. Because of my dementia, I am no longer able to serve on committees or participate in organizations at any level, which has been my life-long passion. It also has made it impossible for me to form new friendships or even maintain old ones.

In terms of my day-to-day life, I have always been a voracious reader. I studied English in college and later taught English classes at the high school level. My favorite books have included literary fiction, creative non-fiction focused on the landscape and environment, poetry (which I have written a little bit of), and the classics of the Western literary canon. I still read, but because of my dementia, I now struggle to retain the material other than briefly.

Further, my energy levels have declined significantly, and I have developed balance and coordination issues that prevent me from enjoying my previous levels of outdoor activity. After a serious hiking accident in 2015 in which I broke my leg and suffered a concussion, I am no longer able to function at the level that allows me to pursue my lifelong passion for the outdoors.

I do not wish to live in a long-term memory care clinic. I watched my mother deteriorate from a vital, active first-grade teacher to simple memory loss to a completely lost soul wandering the hallways of her assisted living facility, unaware of where she was or who her children were. Many hearts were broken, including hers.

I also have serious safety concerns regarding long-term nursing care. Neglect and abuse can occur in even the best facilities. I worried about my mother every day because she was being cared for by strangers. I do not wish to expose myself or my family to that risk.

I understand that stopping eating and drinking will hasten my death. I am committed to this end-of-life option. If I have a stroke or a heart attack or some other type of medical event that makes it impossible for me to carry out my wishes to voluntarily stop eating and drinking, then I want my family, my caregivers, and my medical providers to understand that I absolutely do not consent to being spoon fed by others. If I am personally able to eat/drink and if I have a desire to eat/drink, then I will do so. But if I am unable to eat/drink on my own, then I do not consent to others feeding me by hand or by spoon or by straw.

This Supplemental Statement should be read in conjunction with the Health Care Directive I signed on the first day of February in the year 2017.

I sign of my own free will, being of sound mind.

APPENDIX D: VALUES WORKSHEET

My mom used the worksheet below as she was making decisions and preparing her VSED documentation. You may want to write down your answers and provide copies to your family members and healthcare providers, or use the worksheet as a conversation-starter with your loved ones and/or medical team.

How important to you are the following items? Circle the corresponding number on a scale of 4 (very important) to 0 (not important at all).

Letting nature take its course	4	3	2	1	0
Preserving quality of life	4	3	2	1	0
Staying true to spiritual beliefs/traditions	4	3	2	1	0
Living a long life, regardless of quality	4	3	2	1	0
Being independent	4	3	2	1	0
Being comfortable and pain free	4	3	2	1	0
Leaving good memories for my family	4	3	2	1	0
Making a contribution to medical research	4	3	2	1	0
Being able to relate to family and friends	4	3	2	1	0
Being free of physical limitations	4	3	2	1	0
Being mentally alert and competent	4	3	2	1	0
Being able to leave money to loved ones	4	3	2	1	0
Dying in a short time rather than lingering	4	3	2	1	0
Avoiding expensive care	4	3	2	1	0

Answer the following questions:

What will be important to you when you are dying (e.g. physical comfort, no pain, family members present, etc.)?

How do you feel about the use of life-sustaining measures in the face of terminal illness? Permanent coma? Irreversible chronic illness, such as Alzheimer's disease?

Do you have strong feelings about particular medical procedures? Some procedures to think about include: mechanical breathing (respirator), cardiopulmonary resuscitation (CPR), artificial nutrition and hydration, hospital intensive care, pain relief medication, chemo or radiation therapy, and surgery.

What limitations to your physical and mental health would affect the health care decisions you would make?

Would you want to have financial matters taken into account when treatment decisions are made?

Would you want to be placed in a nursing home if your condition warranted?

Would you prefer Hospice care, with the goal of keeping you comfortable in your home during the final period of your life, as an alternative to hospitalization?

In general, do you wish to participate or share in making decisions about your health care and treatment? Would you always want to know the truth about your condition, treatment options, and the chance of success of treatments?

APPENDIX E: OTHER RESOURCES

ONLINE RESOURCES

VSEDresources.com: The website for VSED Resources Northwest contains a wealth of information assembled by a group of activists dedicated to increasing awareness of VSED, including how-to guides, personal stories, videos, and resource lists. Group members also offer phone, video chat consultations, in-person meetings, and VSED trainings for death doulas and other caregivers.

EndofLifeWA.org: The website for the non-profit group End of Life Washington, which has advocated since 1988 to reform medical practice for the terminally ill, offers guidance and resources for residents of Washington State who choose to pursue VSED.

CV&VN-KNMG VSED/voluntarily stopping eating and drinking: 'caring for people who consciously choose not to eat and drink so as to hasten the end of life' (2014): This PDF publication from the Royal Dutch Medical Association (KNMG), available on their website under the "Publications in English" page of their website, www.knmg.nl, provides a wealth of medical information about supporting patients who choose VSED.

"Overview of voluntarily stopping eating and drinking to hasten death" in the March 2021 volume of the *Annals of Palliative Medicine*: In this article, the authors explore medical, legal, and ethical issues around VSED. They also provide an overview of the limited available research on VSED.

OTHER BOOKS

Voluntarily Stopping Eating and Drinking: A Compassionate, Widely Available Option for Hastening Death edited by Timothy E. Quill, Paul T. Menzel, Thaddeus M. Pope, and Judith K. Schwarz. This book explores various aspects of VSED and includes eight previously unpublished case studies of people who chose VSED.

Choosing to Die: A Personal Story by Phyllis Shacter. Phyllis's memoir and guidebook details how she helped her husband Alan carry out VSED to avoid the late stages of Alzheimer's disease.

Final Gifts: Understanding the Special Awareness, Needs, and Communications of the Dying by Maggie Callanan and Patricia Kelley. The authors, both hospice nurses, provide advice on responding to the requests of the dying and helping them prepare emotionally and spiritually for death.

Cultivating the Doula Heart: Essentials of Compassionate Care by Francesca Arnoldy. Part how-to guide, this book provides a clear framework for supporting those facing hardship, grief, and loss.

YOUR NOTES

ABOUT THE AUTHOR

Kate Christie is a former technical and marketing writer who now works primarily as a novelist. Born and raised in Kalamazoo, Michigan, she studied women's history at Smith College and creative writing at Western Washington University. Currently, she lives near Seattle with her wife, three young daughters, and the family dogs. To connect with Kate, or to learn more about her writing, visit katejchristie.com.

In early 2020, Kate helped her mother Jane successfully escape the late stages of Alzheimer's disease by voluntarily stopping eating and drinking (VSED). During the last ten days of her life, Jane demonstrated that a peaceful, dignified death is possible even when faced with the progressive losses of self and dignity that accompany dementia. This book arose out of Jane's—and Kate's—wish to help others who might choose to leave on their own terms, with their self and personal values intact.

In addition to writing fiction, Kate works with a Western Washington group—VSED Resources Northwest—to promote awareness of and access to VSED. Through this advocacy work, she hopes to honor both her mother's life and her death. If you would like to contribute to VSED Resources Northwest's mission, please visit VSEDresources.com, scroll to the bottom of the page, and click the DONATE button. Your donation is tax deductible and will help VRNW continue to connect with and advocate for the end-of-life community, the terminally ill, and family members of the dying.

Made in the USA
Monee, IL
08 December 2022

20322021R00052